SING AND READ STORYBOOK™
TREASURY™

Amazing Grace, ISBN 0-439-60319-6. Text copyright © 2004 by Scholastic Inc. Illustrations copyright © 2004 by Sylvia Walker. Book design by Madalina S. Blanton.

The Ants Go Marching, ISBN 0-439-26712-9. Text copyright © 2001 by Scholastic Inc. Illustrations copyright © 2001 by Jeffrey Scherer.

Jingle Bells, ISBN 0-439-28721-9. Text copyright © 2001 by Scholastic Inc. Illustrations copyright © 2001 by Darcy May.

She'll Be Coming 'Round the Mountain, ISBN 0-439-43177-8. Copyright © 2003 by Scholastic Inc. Illustrations copyright © 2003 by Chris Demarest.

This Little Light of Mine, ISBN 0-439-46689-X. Text copyright © 2003 by Scholastic Inc. Illustrations copyright © 2003 by Sylvia Walker.

Yankee Doodle, ISBN 0-439-44530-2. Copyright © 2002 by Scholastic Inc. Illustrations copyright © 2002 by Patti Goodnow.

All rights reserved. Published by Scholastic Inc.
SCHOLASTIC, CARTWHEEL BOOKS, SING AND READ STORYBOOK, and associated logos are trademarks and/or registered trademarks of Scholastic Inc.

12 11 10 9 8 7 6 5 4 3 2 1   5 6 7 8 9/0

Printed in the U.S.A.   24

This edition created exclusively for Barnes & Noble, Inc.
2005 Barnes & Noble Books
ISBN 0-7607-6337-2
First compilation printing, February 2005

CONTENTS

AMAZING GRACE

Illustrated by Sylvia Walker

Amazing grace

3

How sweet the sound

4

That saved a soul like me.

I once was lost but now am found.

Was blind but now I see.

'Twas grace that taught my heart to fear
And grace my fears relieved.

How precious did that grace appear
The hour I first believed.

Amazing grace

How sweet the sound

18

That saved a soul like me.

19

I once was lost but now am found.
Was blind but now I see.

A - maz - ing grace, how sweet the

sound to —— save a —— wretch like —— me. ——

—— I —— once was —— lost but now I'm

found. Was — blind but —— now I see. ——

22

THE ANTS GO MARCHING

Illustrated by Jeffrey Scherer

The ants go marching one by one.
Hurrah! Hurrah!
The ants go marching one by one.
Hurrah! Hurrah!

The ants go marching one by one,
the little one stops to suck his thumb,
and they all go marching
down to the ground
to get out of the rain.
BOOM! BOOM! BOOM!

The ants go marching two by two.
Hurrah! Hurrah!
The ants go marching two by two.
Hurrah! Hurrah!
The ants go marching two by two,
the little one stops to tie his shoe,
and they all go marching
down to the ground
to get out of the rain.
BOOM! BOOM! BOOM!

The ants go marching three by three.
Hurrah! Hurrah!
The ants go marching three by three.
Hurrah! Hurrah!

The ants go marching three by three,
the little one stops to ride a bee,
and they all go marching
down to the ground
to get out of the rain.
BOOM! BOOM! BOOM!

The ants go marching four by four.
Hurrah! Hurrah!
The ants go marching four by four.
Hurrah! Hurrah!
The ants go marching four by four,
the little one stops to shut the door,
and they all go marching
down to the ground
to get out of the rain.
BOOM! BOOM! BOOM!

The ants go marching five by five.
Hurrah! Hurrah!
The ants go marching five by five.
Hurrah! Hurrah!

The ants go marching five by five,
the little one stops to jump and jive,
and they all go marching
down to the ground
to get out of the rain.
BOOM! BOOM! BOOM!

The ants go marching six by six.
Hurrah! Hurrah!
The ants go marching six by six.
Hurrah! Hurrah!

The ants go marching six by six,
the little one stops to pick up sticks,
and they all go marching
down to the ground
to get out of the rain.
BOOM! BOOM! BOOM!

The ants go marching seven by seven.
Hurrah! Hurrah!
The ants go marching seven by seven.
Hurrah! Hurrah!

The ants go marching seven by seven,
the little one stops to write with a pen,
and they all go marching
down to the ground
to get out of the rain.
BOOM! BOOM! BOOM!

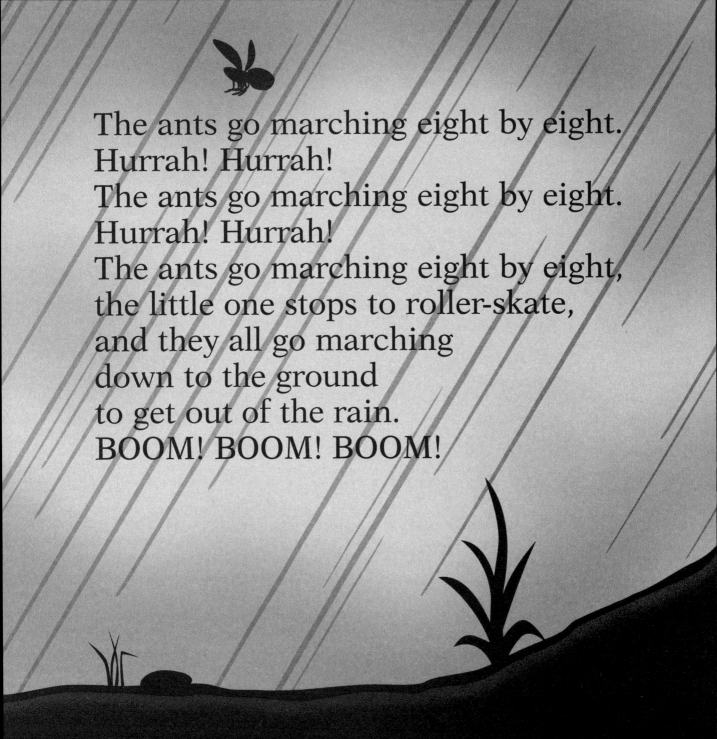

The ants go marching eight by eight.
Hurrah! Hurrah!
The ants go marching eight by eight.
Hurrah! Hurrah!
The ants go marching eight by eight,
the little one stops to roller-skate,
and they all go marching
down to the ground
to get out of the rain.
BOOM! BOOM! BOOM!

The ants go marching nine by nine.
Hurrah! Hurrah!
The ants go marching nine by nine.
Hurrah! Hurrah!

The ants go marching nine by nine,
the little one stops to drink and dine,
and they all go marching
down to the ground
to get out of the rain.
BOOM! BOOM! BOOM!

The ants go marching ten by ten.
Hurrah! Hurrah!
The ants go marching ten by ten.
Hurrah! Hurrah!
The ants go marching ten by ten,
the little one stops to say, "THE END!"
And they all go marching
down to the ground
to get out of the rain.
BOOM! BOOM! BOOM!

JINGLE BELLS

Illustrated by Darcy May

Dashing through the snow

In a one-horse open sleigh,

Through the fields we go

Laughing all the way,

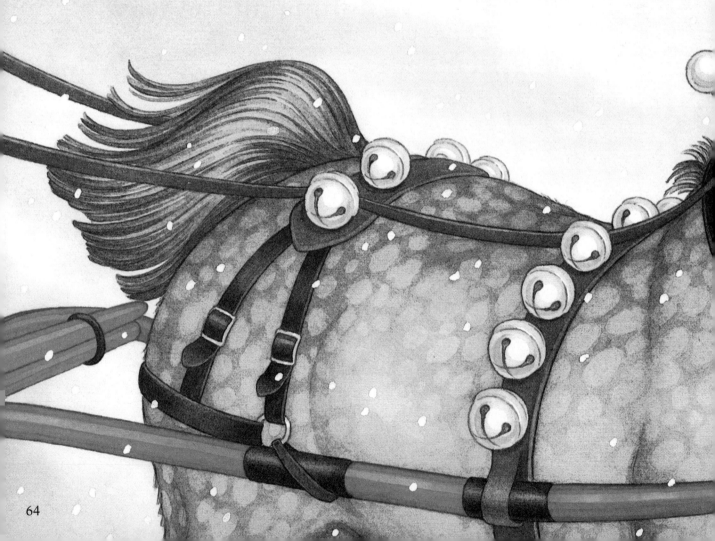

Bells on bobtail ring,

Making spirits bright;

What fun it is to ride and sing
a sleighing song tonight!

Jingle bells! Jingle bells!

Jingle all the way!

Oh, what fun it is to ride

In a one-horse open sleigh.

Ooh!
Jingle bells! Jingle bells!

Jingle all the way!

Oh, what fun it is to ride

83

In a one-horse
open sleigh!

85

JINGLE BELLS

Dash - ing through the snow In a one - horse o - pen sleigh,

Through the fields we go Laugh - ing all the way,

Bells on bob - tail ring, Mak - ing spir - its bright;

What fun it is to ride and sing a sleigh - ing song to - night!

CHORUS

Jin - gle bells! Jin - gle bells! Jin - gle all the way!

Oh, what fun it is to ride In a one - horse o - pen sleigh. Ooh!

Jin - gle bells! Jin - gle bells! Jin - gle all the way!

Oh, what fun it is to ride In a one - horse o - pen sleigh!

SHE'LL BE COMING ROUND THE MOUNTAIN

Illustrated by Chris Demarest

She'll be coming 'round the mountain
when she comes.
She'll be coming 'round the mountain
when she comes.

She'll be coming 'round the mountain.

She'll be coming 'round the mountain.

She'll be coming 'round the mountain
when she comes.

She'll be driving six white horses
when she comes.
She'll be driving six white horses
when she comes.

She'll be driving six white horses.
She'll be driving six white horses.

She'll be driving six white horses
when she comes.

Oh, we'll all go out to meet her
when she comes.
Oh, we'll all go out to meet her
when she comes.

Oh, we'll all go out to meet her.
Oh, we'll all go out to meet her.
Oh, we'll all go out to meet her
when she comes.

And we'll all have chicken and dumplings
when she comes.
And we'll all have chicken and dumplings
when she comes.

And we'll all have chicken and dumplings.
And we'll all have chicken and dumplings.
And we'll all have chicken and dumplings
when she comes.

SHE'LL BE COMING ROUND THE MOUNTAIN

She'll be com-ing 'round the moun-tain when she comes.

She'll be com-ing 'round the moun-tain when she comes.

She'll be com-ing 'round the moun-tain. She'll be com-ing 'round the

moun-tain. She'll be com-ing 'round the moun-tain when she comes.

THIS LITTLE LIGHT OF MINE

Adapted by Rachel Lisberg
Illustrated by Sylvia Walker

This little light of mine,
I'm gonna let it shine.

This little light of mine,
I'm gonna let it shine.
This little light of mine,
I'm gonna let it shine.

Let it shine,
Let it shine,
Let it shine.

I feel it when I'm happy,
I'm gonna let it shine.

I feel it when I'm sad,
I'm gonna let it shine.
I feel it when I'm lonely,
I'm gonna let it shine.

Let it shine,
Let it shine,
Let it shine.

It's with me in the morning,
I'm gonna let it shine.
And in the afternoon,
I'm gonna let it shine.
I feel it in the evening,
I'm gonna let it shine.

Let it shine,
Let it shine,
Let it shine.

121

It's with me every day,
I'm gonna let it shine.
In school, at home, and when I play,
I'm gonna let it shine.
No one can take my light away,
I'm gonna let it shine.

Let it shine,
Let it shine,
Let it shine.

This little light of mine,
I'm gonna let it shine.
This little light of mine,
I'm gonna let it shine.
This little light of mine,
I'm gonna let it shine.

Let it shine,
Let it shine,
Let it shine.

129

THIS LITTLE LIGHT OF MINE

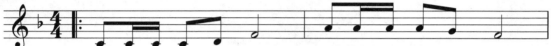

This lit - tle light of mine, I'm gon - na let it shine.

This lit - tle light of mine, I'm gon - na let it shine.

This lit - tle light of mine, I'm gon - na let it shine, let it

shine, let it shine, let it shine.

YANKEE DOODLE

Illustrated by Patti Goodnow

133

Yankee Doodle went to town,

Riding on a pony.

137

Stuck a feather in his cap
And called it macaroni.

Yankee Doodle, keep it up.

Yankee Doodle dandy,

145

Mind the music and the step,

And with the girls be handy.

151

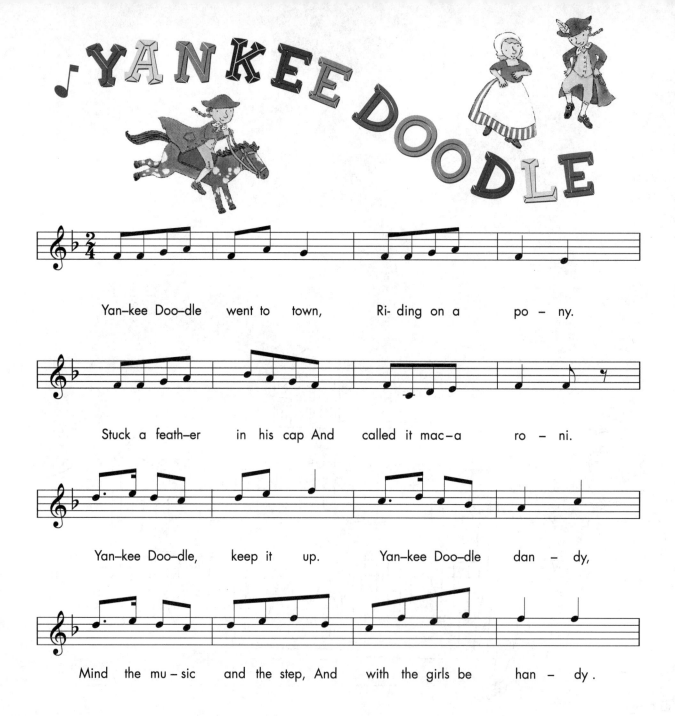

Yan-kee Doo-dle went to town, Ri- ding on a po – ny.

Stuck a feath–er in his cap And called it mac–a ro – ni.

Yan–kee Doo–dle, keep it up. Yan–kee Doo–dle dan – dy,

Mind the mu – sic and the step, And with the girls be han – dy .